contents

e<u>xtra</u> easy days...

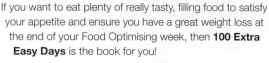

Welcome to **100 Extra Easy Days** – a book that's small in size but huge in Food Optimising ideas for those days when you've run out of enticing new food ideas or just fancy a change. It takes the hassle out of the days when you need to plan in something a bit different, such as entertaining or going out for a meal.

If you want to eat plenty of really tasty, filling food to satisfy your appetite and ensure you have a great weight loss at the end of your Food Optimising week, then **100 Extra Easy Days** is the book for you!

You'll find choices here to suit your mood and the kind of day you're going to have. Whether you're looking for meals that can be prepared quickly (and probably eaten just as fast), dishes that the whole family can enjoy, or if something rich and comforting is what you had in mind, there's a daily menu here that will go down a treat.

100 Extra Easy Days is all about Free Foods and Superfree Foods. If you haven't yet explored these to the full, you'll be truly amazed at how much we encourage you to eat every day, and how easy it is to use these everyday ingredients to create hundreds of family-friendly, slimmer-friendly meals.

We've included some Healthy Extra choices in the menus to make things a little easier for you, and we've made some suggestions on how you could spend your Syns – but feel free to swap these for your personal favourites.

We hope you enjoy 100 Extra Easy Days:
the little book that's packed with
fresh and tasty ideas to put even more
variety into Food Optimising!

your delicious day starts here...

Plan... what you're doing and what you feel like eating for the day; choose a daily menu to suit, and stick to it all day.

Free Foods and Superfree Foods... all these foods are Free – unlimited! – except where we give a serving size. So for example, where fruit and vegetables, chicken and fish, or pasta and rice appear you can eat as much as you like.

Healthy Extra 'a' choices... choose once a day from the list of calcium-rich foods. Some meals have suggestions, marked (a), but feel free to swap these for one of the following:

Milk (for hot drinks, cooking, cereal or to enjoy on its own)
- 350ml skimmed milk
- 250ml semi-skimmed milk
- 175ml whole milk
- 225ml calcium-enriched rice or soya milk

Cheese (for snacks, sandwiches or cooking)
- 30g Cheddar, Emmental, Gouda, Gruyère or Parmesan cheese
- 35g Edam cheese
- 40g reduced fat Cheddar cheese
- 45g feta or mozzarella cheese
- 2 x 25g Dairylea Light Cheese Slices
- 4 x 17.5g Dairylea Light Triangles
- 3 x 17.5g Dairylea Original Triangles
- 6 x 17.5g The Laughing Cow Extra Light Triangles
- 5 x 17.5g The Laughing Cow Light Triangles
- 3 Mini Babybel Light Cheeses
- 2 Mini Babybel Original Cheeses

Healthy Extra 'b' choices... are built into the menus, marked (b).

Syns... you can enjoy between 5 and 15 Syns each day. Some menus have suggestions included, but you can swap these for something else on the list that starts on p146, or for your own choices.

Tips for success

- We recommend that you fill a third of your plate with Superfree Foods and make them your first choice between meals.

- All fresh or frozen fruit is Superfree on Food Optimising, so eat as much as you like.

- Most vegetables are Superfree too and can be fresh, frozen or canned. For good health it's recommended we all eat at least five portions of fruit and vegetables a day; we say have at least that much – more if you like!

- Trim all visible fat off meat and remove any skin from poultry. You can cook it in any way as long as no extra fat is added.

- Drink plenty of liquids: aim to have at least eight glasses a day and vary your drinks to include water or low calorie drinks as well as tea or coffee. Alcohol doesn't count!

- Use fat free vinaigrette* or French-style salad dressings* and all herbs and spices, freely. (*Must be less than 40kcals per 100ml.)

- The following stocks are all Free: all varieties of stock cubes, bouillon cubes/powder, ready-to-use liquid stock, and liquid stock concentrate. Please note that gravy granules or powder and stock granules are not Free.

- If you are cooking pasta, remember that only dried pasta is Free on Extra Easy.

Pork steaks with mustard and
spring onion mash, pg 18

A selection from our…

gastro pub

Great gastro pub grub without the gastronomical prices

As the nights draw in we crave comfort food: warming breakfasts, wholesome lunches and hearty homemade suppers – and help is at hand. From kippers and scrambled eggs to sausages and mash and a gammon grill, we've got 'eating inn' covered.

pep it up!

breakfast

Tasty scrambled eggs

Cook chopped spring onion, green peppers and tomato in low calorie cooking spray until softened. Add a couple of lightly beaten eggs with a pinch of garlic powder and cook until lightly scrambled. Season with soy sauce and serve on 2 slices of wholemeal toast (b).

lunch

Rice stuffed peppers

Cook some chopped onion and add a spoonful of dried mixed herbs and some paprika. Mix into cooked rice, red kidney beans and sweetcorn and spoon into pepper halves. Bake them for 45 minutes at 180°C/ Gas 4, until tender. Serve with a large mixed salad. Enjoy a couple of peaches for pud.

dinner

Sausage & 'mash'

Enjoy homemade mustard sausages & colcannon (see recipe on page 10). Follow with some fresh strawberries topped with fat free natural yogurt.

close to the wedge

breakfast

Cereal & minty melon

Enjoy 35g fruit & fibre (b) with milk (a) and a minty melon salad (mix cubes of watermelon, honeydew and cantaloupe melon with shredded mint leaves).

lunch

Chicken & bacon salad with a sweet twist

Toss together cooked new potatoes and baby salad leaves with sliced cooked skinless chicken and cooked pieces of lean back bacon. Add halved grapes and chunks of fresh peach and serve with fat free French dressing.

dinner

Steak with potato wedges & roast tomatoes

Cut one large potato per person into wedges and place in a roasting tin. Spray them with low calorie cooking spray, add seasoning and a pinch of paprika and roast in the oven at 200°C/Gas 6 until cooked through, about 40 minutes. Add small tomatoes on the vine half way through. Season lean steaks and cook on a griddle or non-stick frying pan to your liking. Serve with the wedges and roast tomatoes and a large salad.

homemade mustard sausages and colcannon

Ready in 40 minutes

Serves 4

½ **Syn** per serving on Extra Easy

500g Tesco Extra Lean Pork Mince

1 large egg, beaten

1 garlic clove, crushed

4 spring onions, finely chopped

2 level tsp English mustard

salt and freshly ground black pepper

900g potatoes, peeled

275ml vegetable stock

300g Savoy cabbage,
finely shredded

1. Mix the pork mince in a bowl with the egg, garlic, spring onions and mustard. Season and mix well. Roll the mixture into 12 sausage shapes and chill them for at least 15 minutes.

2. Meanwhile, cook the potatoes in lightly salted boiling water for 25 minutes. Drain and leave to steam dry in a colander.

3. Pour the stock into a saucepan and bring to the boil. Add the cabbage and cook, covered, for 5 minutes. Add the potatoes to the cabbage and stock and mash thoroughly. Season to taste and keep warm.

4. Cook the sausages in low calorie cooking spray for 15 minutes, turning frequently so they brown evenly. Check they are cooked through.

5. Serve with the colcannon and boiled carrots and cauliflower or vegetables of your choice.

lucky duck

breakfast

Smoked haddock & egg kedgeree

Cook long grain rice in water with a spoonful of mild curry powder. Drain and mix with cooked smoked haddock and quartered hard-boiled eggs. Enjoy 2 Weetabix (b) with milk (a) while it's cooking.

lunch

Griddled vegetables with pasta

Thinly slice courgettes and aubergine (1 of each per person) into long lengths. Preheat a griddle and cook the vegetables for 6-8 minutes, turning to make griddle marks. Add them to a bowl and sprinkle with the juice of 1-2 lemons and some seasoning. Add cooked pasta and some torn basil.

dinner

5-spice duck stir-fry

Thinly slice skinless duck breast fillets and coat in 5-spice powder. Heat a large wok and spray with low calorie cooking spray. Cook the spiced duck for a few minutes, stirring before adding a large bag of mixed stir-fry vegetables and cooking for a few minutes until done. Add a squeeze of lime juice and serve with cooked rice.

pure and simple

breakfast

Plum & nectarine compôte

Place slices of ripe, stoned plums and nectarines in a bowl and sprinkle with sweetener. Mix 3 tbsp quark with lemon juice and sweetener to taste and serve with the fruit. Follow with 2 slices of wholemeal toast (b) topped with honey (1 Syn per level tsp).

lunch

Meaty chilli & rice

Dry fry extra lean minced beef in a non-stick pan, add chopped onion, red peppers, mushrooms and chilli powder to taste and cook until soft, then add canned tomatoes and red kidney beans and simmer for 25-30 minutes. Serve with boiled rice and a large mixed salad.

dinner

Salmon & new potatoes

Grill salmon steaks and serve with a topping of chopped red pepper, capers and parsley and lots of boiled new potatoes, broccoli and green beans. Finish with slices of melon and a Free Müllerlight Yogurt.

prawn again

breakfast

Potato sauté

Sauté lots of cooked potato slices in low calorie cooking spray and serve with baked beans, mushrooms and an egg or two fried in low calorie cooking spray.

lunch

Half pint prawns with lemon

Fill a large glass with whole unpeeled cooked prawns and serve with 2 slices of wholemeal bread (b) and plenty of lemon wedges. Accompany with a big side salad.

dinner

Gammon grill

Grill a lean gammon steak and serve with new potatoes and lots of vegetables, such as carrots, green beans and broccoli. Have a banana and some pineapple for afters.

Spicy beefburgers and sweet potato chips with chutney, opposite

Moroccan burger king

breakfast

Grilled kippers

Grill kippers and serve with grilled tomatoes and mushrooms.

lunch

Moroccan couscous

Make up a pack of Ainsley Harriott Moroccan Medley Couscous (1½ Syns per packet) and serve with a large crisp mixed salad. Follow with a Free Müllerlight Yogurt.

dinner

Spicy beefburgers & sweet potato chips with chutney

Cook parboiled sweet potato chips in a preheated oven at 240°C/Gas 9 for 20-25 minutes. Make the chutney: put chopped tomatoes, onion, chopped apple (2½ Syns each when cooked), garlic and balsamic vinegar in a saucepan, cover and cook over a high heat for 5 minutes. Uncover and cook for a further 5 minutes. Season well. Mix together extra lean minced beef, mustard powder and chilli flakes. Season and mix well. Shape into four burgers. Cook the burgers in low calorie cooking spray over a medium heat, for 7 minutes on each side. Serve in 60g wholemeal rolls (b). Follow with a melon, grape and kiwi fruit salad.

it's a wrap

breakfast

Brunch ham & egg wrap

Whisk 2 eggs and cook in a small non-stick frying pan, turn and cook the omelette on the other side. Place on a plate and arrange a couple of slices of lean ham on top. Place a handful of watercress down the middle with a thinly sliced small tomato and roll up to eat.

Potato rosti with bacon, opposite

lunch

Prawn salad

Mix lots of crispy iceberg lettuce, cucumber, tomatoes and juicy prawns with Kraft Light Thousand Island Dressing (1 Syn per level tbsp), and a squeeze of lemon juice. Serve with a 60g wholemeal roll (b).

dinner

Beef braise & balsamic cabbage

Soften chopped onion with cubed lean braising steak. Add a pack of chopped root casserole vegetables. Cover with beef stock, add some Marmite and cook, covered, simmering for about 2 hours. Roast shredded red cabbage in a hot oven with some seasoning and a good drizzle of balsamic vinegar, stirring frequently until cooked through.

nice 'n' spice

breakfast

Potato rosti with bacon

Fry chopped lean bacon in a little low calorie cooking spray until crisp. Add to cooked and grated potatoes. Cook onion until soft then add to the potatoes and bacon. Add chives and seasoning and mix well. Shape into patties and cook in low calorie cooking spray for 2-3 minutes on each side. Serve with oven roasted vine tomatoes and mushrooms.

lunch

Smoked haddock & egg salad

Steam or microwave a piece of smoked haddock and poach an egg per serving. Serve the fish and egg on top of a large salad of cucumber, lettuce, tomatoes, beetroot and spring onions.

dinner

Spicy pork with courgette & dill couscous

Roast chunks of courgette in the oven at 220°C/Gas 7 until soft. Roll lean pork fillets in a spice mix (lemon zest, oregano, cumin, paprika and salt) until evenly coated. Cook the pork on a griddle for 20 minutes over a medium heat, turning frequently. Place in the oven for a further 10 minutes. Remove and cover with foil and allow to rest for five minutes. Prepare couscous according to the packet instructions. Stir in the courgette chunks and some chopped dill. Serve with the pork and some carrots and green beans. Follow with a 225g baked apple topped with 1 level tbsp of mincemeat (b) and fat free natural yogurt.

chops away

breakfast

Simply oats

35g Unflavoured porridge oats, made with milk (a) and topped with some fresh berries of your choice.

lunch

Smoked salmon, dill & cucumber salad

Peel a cucumber and thinly slice. Add some lemon juice and chopped dill to the cucumber. Serve with smoked salmon slices and some salad leaves and salad cress.

dinner

Pork steaks with mustard & spring onion mash

Spread lean pork steaks with a mixture of crushed garlic and chopped sage. Season and marinate for 2-3 hours. Spray the steaks with low calorie cooking spray and cook on a very hot griddle for 6-8 minutes on each side. Boil chopped butternut squash for 15 minutes. Drain and mash. Stir in chopped spring onions, a little mustard powder and some fat free natural fromage frais. Season well. Serve with green cabbage.

good for a griddle!

breakfast

Weetabix & melon
2 Weetabix (b) with milk (a) followed by a wedge of melon.

lunch

Grazing board
On a wooden board arrange cooked, sliced meats such as trimmed Parma ham (½ Syn per slice), deli turkey, lean pastrami and smoked ham with small cherry tomatoes on the vine, cornichons, radishes, pickled onions and a large mixed salad. Follow with a bunch of grapes and a Free Müllerlight Yogurt.

dinner

Griddled vegetable salad with lemon chicken & new potatoes
Cut courgettes and aubergines into long lengthways strips and griddle in batches for 5 minutes. Marinade flattened out chicken fillets in lemon juice and black pepper while the veg cook and then griddle the chicken until cooked. Serve the vegetables and chicken with new potatoes.

Chargrilled steak
with rainbow salad,
pg 23

everyday easy

Spend less time in the kitchen and more time enjoying life!

Super-filling, super-tasty and ready in less time than it takes to heat up a ready meal, these quick to make culinary delights are delicious any day of the week.

brilliant *bangers*

breakfast

Strawberry crunch

Mix 35g Weetabix Crunchy Bran (b) with fat free natural yogurt and plenty of chopped strawberries.

lunch

Tuna sweetcorn salad

Drain a can of tuna in spring water and mix with sliced spring onions, a can of drained sweetcorn, chopped red pepper and diced hard-boiled egg. Add a spoonful of fat free natural yogurt and season to taste. Serve dolloped on top of torn lettuce leaves.

dinner

Sausage & mash

Grill Quorn Best Ever Sausages (1 Syn each) and serve with mashed potatoes, vegetables of your choice and onion gravy: add onions sautéed in low calorie cooking spray to gravy made from granules (1½ Syns per 100ml).

surf and turf

breakfast

Fruity crunch

Have 35g Nestlé Fruitful Shredded Wheat (b) with milk (a) served with sliced banana.

lunch

Salsa fish

Make the salsa by mixing chopped tomatoes, finely chopped red chilli and grated ginger. Serve with cooked white fish fillets, boiled rice and a large side salad.

dinner

Chargrilled steak with rainbow salad

Rub the cut sides of a garlic clove over both sides of a large lean beef steak and season well. Griddle the steak on each side until cooked to your liking. Serve with a fluffy jacket potato and a rainbow salad of mixed leaves, sliced cucumber, halved cherry tomatoes, grated carrot, drained canned sweetcorn and thinly shredded red cabbage. For dessert have a sparkling fruit cocktail – chunks of fresh exotic fruit with diet lemonade and low calorie tropical fruit cordial.

wham bam ham!

breakfast

Tomato scramble

Make lots of scrambled egg and serve with plenty of grilled tomatoes and mushrooms. Follow with a Free Müllerlight Yogurt.

lunch

Ham salad sandwich

Fill 2 slices of wholemeal bread (b) with lots of sliced lean ham, crispy iceberg lettuce, cucumber and sliced red onion. Follow with an orange and some grapes.

dinner

Tuna pasta bake

Place partially cooked penne pasta in an ovenproof dish, add a can of drained kidney beans, a can of drained sweetcorn, a can of drained tuna in spring water, finely sliced spring onion and red pepper strips. Stir in 200ml of water and the juice of 1 lemon. Season and mix well. Bake in a preheated oven at 200°C/Gas 6 for 20 minutes and serve with green beans. Follow with a bowl of mixed berries.

pitta and pasta

breakfast

Chocolate on toast

Top 2 slices of wholemeal toast (b) with chocolate spread (1½ Syns per level tsp). Follow with a huge bowl of fresh blackcurrants, blackberries and raspberries topped with fat free natural yogurt.

lunch

Prawn cocktail pitta

Mix fat free natural yogurt with tomato purée and add small cooked and peeled prawns. Stuff a mini pitta bread (4 Syns) with the prawns and serve with a large mixed salad.

dinner

Turkey tagliatelle bolognese

Enjoy a serving of turkey tagliatelle bolognese (see recipe on the next page). Follow with chunks of fresh fruit smothered in fat free natural yogurt.

Tuna pasta bake, opposite

turkey tagliatelle bolognese

Ready in 45 minutes

Serves 4

Free on Extra Easy

1 onion, chopped

1 carrot, finely chopped

175g mushrooms, chopped

low calorie cooking spray

500g extra lean turkey breast mince

150g lean bacon medallions, finely cut

400g can chopped tomatoes

a pinch of chilli flakes

375g dried tagliatelle pasta

a small handful of flat-leaf parsley
leaves, roughly chopped

1. Gently cook the onion, carrot and mushrooms in low calorie cooking spray in a large covered saucepan for 10 minutes. Turn up the heat, add the turkey mince and bacon and stir until browned all over, for about 5 minutes.

2. Add the chopped tomatoes and chilli flakes with 150ml of water and bring to a simmer. Cook gently, covered, for 20 minutes.

3. Meanwhile, cook the pasta according to the packet instructions. Drain well. Scatter the parsley over the bolognese and serve with the tagliatelle and plenty of mixed salad or vegetables of your choice.

feeling fruity

breakfast

Beans & mushrooms on toast

Cook large field mushrooms under the grill for 10 minutes. Warm baked beans, add a squirt of tomato purée and serve with the mushrooms on 2 slices of wholemeal toast (b).

lunch

Fruity chicken & rice

Mix cooked skinless chicken chunks with boiled rice and fresh orange segments, diced apple, halved grapes and diced cucumber. Follow with a banana.

dinner

Chunky tuna niçoise salad

Mix cooked and halved baby new potatoes, blanched green beans, little gem lettuce leaves, halved cherry tomatoes, diced cucumber and sliced red onion in a large bowl. Add flaked, drained tuna in spring water, pour over fat free salad dressing and top with halved hard-boiled eggs. Have some apples and pears for dessert.

finger on the pulse

breakfast

Weetabix & fruit

Have 2 Weetabix (b) with milk (a). Follow
with juicy segments of orange and grapefruit.

lunch

Spiced lentil soup

Place onions, carrots, garlic, red chilli,
lentils, ground coriander, ground turmeric
and ground cumin in a large saucepan.
Add vegetable stock and bring to the boil.
Simmer until the lentils are tender. Season
and liquidise before serving.

dinner

Pork with mustard onions

Thinly slice 2 large onions and cook in a
little stock until they soften and start to
caramelise. Add some sweetener towards
the end with a dash of Worcestershire sauce
and a spoonful of mustard (½ Syn per level
tsp). Serve with lean pork chops, grilled to
your liking, vegetables and new potatoes.
Have fresh fruit for afters.

noodle doodle

breakfast

Banana bran

Have 35g Kellogg's All-Bran (b) with milk (a) and top with lots of sliced banana.

lunch

Omelette with prawns & chives

Make a large fluffy omelette and top with chives and cooked and peeled prawns. Serve with mushrooms and tomatoes.

dinner

Stir-fried beef with noodles

Stir-fry strips of lean beef in low calorie cooking spray for 3-4 minutes. Remove from the pan, set aside and keep warm. Add finely sliced onion to the pan with finely sliced garlic, chopped red chilli, red pepper strips, a can of drained water chestnuts, mangetout and bean sprouts. Stir-fry for 4-5 minutes. Add soy sauce and cook for 3-4 minutes. Return the beef to the pan and cook for a further 3-4 minutes. Serve with cooked egg noodles. Follow with The Skinny Cow Ice Cream Lolly, any variety, 110ml (4½ Syns).

super *hoops*

breakfast

Bangers & beans

Grill Quorn Best Ever Sausages (1 Syn each) and serve with grilled mushrooms, tomatoes and baked beans. Enjoy slices of melon while they're cooking.

lunch

Hoops on toast

Smother 2 slices of wholemeal toast (b) with spaghetti hoops. Follow with lots of sliced banana topped with fat free natural fromage frais and sprinkled with cinnamon.

dinner

Lamb dinner

Cook lean lamb steaks to your liking and serve with new potatoes, spring greens, carrots and cauliflower. Pour over gravy made from granules (1½ Syns per 100ml) and serve with some no added sugar mint sauce.

simply salmon

breakfast

Mixed fruit salad

Mix chopped nectarines, pineapple, kiwi fruit and apple in a bowl. Top with fat free natural fromage frais and sprinkle with cinnamon and nutmeg.

lunch

Salmon & satsumas

Serve strips of smoked salmon with a yogurt dressing (fat free natural yogurt with the juice of ½ lemon and some chopped dill) and accompany with a large mixed salad and a 60g wholemeal roll (b). Follow with a couple of satsumas.

dinner

Pasta with spinach & bacon

Cook pasta according to the packet instructions. Meanwhile, in a large frying pan, cook lean diced smoked bacon and add a little crushed garlic. Add a bag of baby leaf spinach and a little of the pasta cooking water and leave to wilt. Drain the pasta and mix into the spinach and bacon.

bean there, *done* that

breakfast

Fruity brekkie bowl

Defrost frozen mixed tropical fruit and mix in 30g Nestlé Honey Nut Shredded Wheat (b) and a sliced banana. Serve with fat free natural yogurt.

lunch

5-bean salad

Mix a can of mixed bean salad with cooked green beans and lots of halved cherry tomatoes. Add a drizzle of balsamic vinegar and some torn basil, if you like. Serve with some sliced cooked lean deli ham or turkey. Have some sliced fresh pineapple for afters.

dinner

Oriental salmon in foil

Place salmon fillets on squares of foil. Top with thinly sliced red pepper and red onion and drizzle liberally with soy sauce and a squeeze of lime juice. Wrap tightly and place on a baking tray. Cook in a preheated oven at 190°C/Gas 5 for 20-25 minutes. Serve with cooked egg noodles.

FOOD IN A FLASH

Make it easy on yourself ...

Are you in a rush? Do you need a quick food fix? Stock your cupboards with standby staples and enjoy these fresh and fabulous daily menus – all the hard work's been done for you! From speedy saucy spaghetti with no cook sauce to uncomplicated couscous to quick pasta carbonara, losing weight really is as simple as 1,2,3…

Roasted vegetable couscous, pg 45

QUICK CUISINE

breakfast

Fruity crunch

Swirl 35g Weetabix Crunchy Bran (b) into fat free natural yogurt along with lots of fresh fruit chunks.

lunch

Crab noodles

Mix drained white crab meat in brine with cooked dried noodles. Add chopped red chilli, lime zest, flat-leaf parsley and a squeeze of lime juice to taste. Serve with a rocket salad. Follow with lots of watermelon.

dinner

Quick pasta 'carbonara'

Make up a pack of Batchelors Cheese, Leek & Ham Pasta 'n' Sauce with water (1 Syn) and serve with a large mixed salad. Follow with Total 0% Fat Greek Yogurt topped with sliced banana.

BERRY BONANZA

breakfast

Summer start

Smother fresh summer berries in your favourite Free Müllerlight Yogurt and sprinkle over 35g bran flakes (b).

lunch

Fruity rice salad

Mix lots of boiled rice with fat free natural yogurt, spring onion and chunks of fresh peach, pineapple and kiwi fruit.

dinner

Salmon supper

Grill or microwave a salmon fillet and serve with broccoli, green beans and canned new potatoes sprinkled with fresh mint.

SPUD u LIKE

breakfast

Bacon sarnie

Fill 2 slices of wholemeal bread (b) with lots of grilled lean bacon and top with brown sauce or tomato ketchup (1 Syn per level tbsp). Enjoy wedges of melon while the bacon's cooking.

lunch

Jacket & beans

Top a jacket potato with lots of baked beans and serve with a large mixed salad. Drizzle some Worcestershire sauce over the beans for an extra kick.

dinner

Beef & black bean stir-fry

Stir-fry some thinly sliced lean rump steak until browned, add some sliced onions and green peppers and a sachet of Amoy Straight to Wok Aromatic Black Bean Stir Fry Sauce (4½ Syns for a 120g sachet). Serve with plenty of Batchelors Chinese Savoury Rice.

SPEEDY FEASTS

breakfast

Tomatoes on toast

Top 2 slices of wholemeal toast (b)
with canned plum tomatoes. Follow
with a citrus salad of fresh orange
and grapefruit segments.

lunch

Moroccan tabbouleh salad

Mix prepared bulgur wheat with chopped red
and green pepper, cucumber, red grapes and
crushed garlic. Season well, squeeze over
some lemon juice and serve with a green
salad. Follow with an apple or two.

dinner

Noodle supper

Prepare a pack of Batchelors Low Fat Sweet
Thai Chilli Super Noodles and serve with
stir-fried bean sprouts, mangetout and baby
sweetcorn. Follow with fresh berries layered
in a tall glass with fat free natural yogurt.

WELSH *RAREBIT*

breakfast

'Fry-up'

Grill lots of lean bacon and serve with grilled mushrooms and tomatoes and an egg (or two) fried in low calorie cooking spray.

lunch

Cheese on toast

Top 2 slices of wholemeal toast (b) with 40g reduced fat Cheddar cheese (a), grill until bubbling and serve with a large mixed salad. Follow with a 120g pot Danone Shape Delights 0% Yogurt, any variety (½ Syn), a peach and an orange.

dinner

Moroccan chicken

Top skinless chicken fillets with lemon juice, cumin, cinnamon and paprika and grill until cooked. Serve with couscous mixed with chopped red onion, tomatoes, garlic, chopped flat-leaf parsley and mint.

TZATZIKI TREAT

breakfast

Fruit & yogurt

Smother chunks of apple, pear and banana in your favourite Free Müllerlight Yogurt.

lunch

Beef & beetroot with tzatziki salad

Make the tzatziki by mixing together cubed cucumber, sliced mint and fat free natural yogurt. Mix strips of lean cooked beef with chopped beetroot and serve on a bed of salad leaves with the tzatziki. Accompany with a jacket potato, cooked in the microwave for speed.

dinner

Mezze platter

Enjoy a generous serving of the mezze platter of red pepper houmous and tuna tapenade, (see recipe on next page).

MEZZE PLATTER

Ready in 20 minutes

Serves 4

1 Syn per serving on Extra Easy

for the houmous
400g can chickpeas, drained
1 garlic clove, crushed
zest of 1 lemon
juice of 2 lemons
½ tsp ground cumin
40g bottled, roasted peppers in brine
salt and freshly ground black pepper

for the tapenade
50g black kalamata olives, pitted
15g anchovies, drained and rinsed
20g flat-leaf parsley, plus extra to garnish
1 garlic clove, crushed
185g can tuna in brine, drained
juice of 1 lemon

1. To make the houmous, blitz together the chickpeas, garlic, lemon zest and juice, ground cumin and peppers in a food processor until well chopped. Add 6 tablespoons of water and blitz to a purée, season to taste and transfer to a serving bowl.

2. Make the tapenade by blitzing together the olives, anchovies, parsley and garlic until very finely chopped. Add the tuna and lemon juice with some seasoning and pulse until mixed well. Transfer to a serving bowl and scatter with the remaining parsley.

3. To assemble your mezze platter, arrange cherry tomatoes on the vine, sliced green pepper, sticks of carrot and celery and sliced meats such as prosciutto (½ Syn per slice) and lean cooked ham on a large marble or wooden board and place the dishes of houmous and tapenade alongside. Serve with 6 Ryvita Wholegrain Crackerbread per person (b).

BRILLIANT BURGERS

breakfast

Salmon & scrambled eggs

Make lots of scrambled egg and serve with slices of smoked salmon and grilled tomatoes.

lunch

Ham & potato salad

Mix a can of drained new potatoes with chunks of lean ham, chopped red apple, spring onions, celery and fat free natural fromage frais. Season and serve scattered with chopped dill. Follow with a banana and a nectarine.

dinner

Quarter pounder

Grill a Sainsbury's Butcher's Choice Chargrilled Beef Quarter Pounder (5 Syns each) and serve in a 60g wholemeal roll (b) filled with crisp iceberg lettuce, sliced beef tomatoes and sliced gherkins, accompanied with canned new potatoes and a large mixed salad.

TASTES OF THE MED

breakfast

Banana starter

Slice a banana or two, drizzle over fat free natural yogurt and top with 35g Dorset Cereals Simply Delicious Muesli (b).

lunch

Chunky omelette

Cook an omelette and fill with chopped canned potatoes, onion and cooked lean bacon. Serve with a large mixed salad. Follow with a bunch of grapes and some fresh cherries.

dinner

Roasted vegetable couscous

Place chunks of red and yellow pepper, aubergine, courgette and red onion on a baking tray with some crushed garlic, spray with low calorie cooking spray and roast in the oven at 220°C/Gas 7 for 15-20 minutes. Cook some couscous in vegetable stock and add mixed fresh herbs of your choice. Top with the roasted vegetables.

SIZZLE AND SERVE

breakfast

Beans & egg on toast

Smother 2 slices of wholemeal toast (b) with baked beans and top with a poached egg and chopped parsley. Follow with a banana.

lunch

Garden salad with turkey

Serve lean deli slices of roast turkey with watercress, shredded iceberg lettuce, sliced peppers, tomatoes, cucumber, sliced red onion and chopped cress and drizzle with fat free French dressing.

dinner

Steak & stir-fry

Grill a lean sirloin steak and top with lots of stir-fried vegetables and noodles cooked with soy sauce and chopped fresh ginger.

FASTA PASTA

breakfast

Fruity porridge

Make up 35g plain porridge oats (b) with milk (a) and top with fresh berries.

lunch

Spaghetti with tomato & basil no-cook sauce

Boil some quick-cook spaghetti. Meanwhile finely chop some vine tomatoes and mix with plenty of freshly chopped basil and a splash of red wine vinegar. Drain the spaghetti and stir the tomato sauce through.

dinner

Chicken tikka & rice

Cook some Birds Eye frozen Vegetable Rice (½ Syn per 100g) and top with Asda/Co-op/Sainsbury's/Tesco Chicken Tikka Fillets.

Gremolata cod &
Slimming World chips, pg 56

simple family food

Fabulous feasts for the days when you want harmony, not hassle at the table...

None of the family-friendly recipes in this section take more than 30 minutes to prepare and cook – and they're all made with easy-to-find ingredients for the days when life gets in the way of your best-laid shopping plans.

slam in the lamb

breakfast
Melon boats with fruit

Quarter and deseed a cantaloupe melon
and chop up the flesh. Mix the melon with
a handful of seedless and halved grapes
and some raspberries and spoon back
in the melon shells to serve.

lunch
Salmon & cucumber roll

Mix canned, drained salmon with sliced cucumber,
some very finely sliced red onion and a little
Tabasco and fill a 60g wholemeal roll (b), adding
some shredded lettuce too. Serve with
a handful of cherry tomatoes.

dinner
Lamb cutlets with couscous

Mix cooked couscous with plenty of chopped
herbs like parsley, mint and dill and chopped
fresh tomatoes. Grill some lean lamb cutlets to
your liking. Serve the couscous and lamb with
some wilted spinach.

Seared beef salad, opposite

fancy a ruby?

breakfast
Eggs on toast

Serve poached eggs on 2 slices of wholemeal toast (b). Follow with a Free Müllerlight Yogurt.

lunch
Seared beef salad

Mix strips of cooked, lean sirloin steak with boiled halved new potatoes. Add halved cherry tomatoes, cucumber strips and chopped parsley. Drizzle over a warm dressing of cider vinegar, sweetener and crushed pink peppercorns.

dinner
Prawn curry

Gently soften sliced onion in low calorie cooking spray with finely chopped garlic, green chilli, red and green peppers and add a couple of tsp of garam masala and a tsp of turmeric for the final couple of minutes. Add a cup of fish stock and let it bubble away until the onion is soft and the liquid reduced a little. Add raw or ready-cooked large prawns and heat until cooked and thoroughly heated through. Serve with basmati rice and chopped coriander. Follow with a bowl of strawberries topped with fat free natural yogurt.

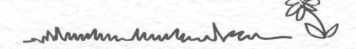

jazz it up!

breakfast
Mushroom omelette

Make a large fluffy omelette filled with chopped mushrooms and serve with tomatoes and grilled lean bacon.

lunch
Jazzed up beans on toast

Heat a can of baked beans, adding a little tomato purée to thicken the sauce slightly, a dash of Worcestershire sauce, some seasoning and a small sprinkling of mixed herbs. Layer some lean ham onto 2 slices of wholemeal toast (b) and spoon on the beans. Finish with a dash of Tabasco or dried chilli flakes if you like. Enjoy a fresh fruit salad topped with fat free natural yogurt for pud.

dinner
Spicy chicken fried rice

Grill some skinless chicken breasts for 10-12 minutes on each side or until cooked through. Tear into bite-sized chunks. Heat a wok sprayed with low calorie cooking spray. Add some cooked rice, red chilli, garlic, ginger and 5-spice powder and stir-fry for 4 minutes. Add the chicken, red and yellow peppers, shredded pak choi, spring onions, bean sprouts, light soy sauce and freshly ground black pepper and fry for another 4 minutes. Push the ingredients to one side of the pan. Add a beaten egg to the other side and leave for about 10 seconds until it starts to set. Break up the egg with a fork, stir through the other ingredients and serve.

sizzle and serve

breakfast
Bacon, egg & tomato roll

Grill slices of lean back bacon and serve in a 60g wholemeal roll (b) with a fried egg, cooked in low calorie cooking spray, and a sliced tomato.

lunch
Quick tuna pasta

Mix drained tuna (in brine/spring water) with diced red pepper, spring onions, grated courgette and cooked pasta bows. Add lime juice and seasoning.

dinner
Peri-peri burger, Slimming World chips & slaw

Enjoy a peri-peri burger with chips and slaw (see recipe on next page) with a glass of lager (4½ Syns per 250ml). Follow with a huge bowl of strawberries topped with fat free natural fromage frais.

Spicy chicken fried rice, opposite

peri-peri burger with chips and slaw

Ready in 45 minutes

Serves 4

1 Syn per serving on Extra Easy

900g potatoes, peeled

low calorie cooking spray

salt and freshly ground black pepper

500g pack extra lean minced beef

1 small red pepper, finely chopped

1 tsp each of garlic powder,
oregano and ground cumin

½ tsp cayenne pepper

275g red cabbage, finely shredded

½ small onion, very finely chopped

1 red skinned apple, coarsely grated

75g each of extra light mayonnaise and
fat free natural fromage frais

1. Preheat the oven to 220°C/Gas 7. Cut the potatoes into chips and boil in a large pan of lightly salted boiling water for 5 minutes and drain. Return to the pan, replace the lid and shake to roughen the edges of the chips (to help them crisp up).

2. Line a baking sheet with non-stick baking parchment and spread out the chips. Spray with low calorie cooking spray and sprinkle with salt. Place in the oven and bake for 15-20 minutes.

3. Preheat the grill to its highest setting. In a large bowl, mix together the minced beef, red pepper and the spices with some seasoning. Shape into 4 large burgers and cook under the grill for 15 minutes.

4. Make the coleslaw by mixing the red cabbage, onion, apple, mayonnaise and fromage frais in a bowl with some seasoning.

fish supper

breakfast
On the run

Grab 1 Slimming World Hi-fi Bar, any variety (b), with some plums and a clementine.

lunch
Chunky chicken pasta salad

Put strips of mixed peppers and thinly sliced onions in a deep non-stick frying pan and cover. Turn up the heat until it sizzles, lower the heat and cook for 15 minutes. Add crushed garlic and cook for a further 10 minutes. Sprinkle in red wine vinegar and seasoning. Remove from the heat. Mix with cooled boiled pasta, cooked skinless chicken breast chunks and chopped parsley and basil.

dinner
Gremolata cod & Slimming World chips

Make the gremolata by mixing lemon zest, chopped parsley, fennel seeds and oregano with some seasoning. Spoon on top of cod fillets and pat down gently. Bake in the oven for 20-25 minutes at 200°C/Gas 6. Make some tartare sauce by mixing chopped parsley with shallot, gherkin, capers, extra light mayonnaise (1 Syn per level tbsp) and fat free natural fromage frais. Serve the cod with Slimming World chips (see recipe on page 54), garden peas and tartare sauce. Follow with a couple of satsumas.

grills and frills

breakfast
Banana berry cereal

Mix 35g Weetabix Crunchy Bran (b)
with sliced banana and some raspberries
and serve with milk (a).

lunch
Burger & wedges

Cut a potato per serving into wedges, place
in a roasting tin and spray with low calorie
cooking spray. Bake them at 200°C/Gas
6 for 40 minutes. Mix a pack of extra lean
minced beef with a little tomato purée and
some very finely chopped spring onion.
Shape into burgers and grill for 8-10 minutes,
turning until cooked through. Serve with a big
colourful salad.

dinner
Lamb chops with mint yogurt

Rub lean lamb chops with dried mint and
some salt. Cook them under a preheated grill
for 10 minutes, turning. Mix chopped fresh
mint and spring onions into fat free natural
yogurt. Serve the lamb chops with the mint
yogurt, jacket potatoes and a large salad.

Chunky chicken
pasta salad,
opposite

speedy Gonzales

breakfast
Bite-sized breakfast

Have 35g Nestlé Bitesize Shredded Wheat
(b), topped with lots of fresh raspberries and
served with milk (a).

Spaghetti with meatballs, opposite

lunch
Tuna jacket

Fill a large jacket potato with drained tuna
in spring water, drained sweetcorn and extra
light mayonnaise (1 Syn per level tbsp).
Serve with lettuce, cucumber and tomato.
Grab a banana for afters.

dinner
Sizzling pepper & chicken fajitas

Sprinkle chicken strips and slices of mixed
peppers and onion with a tsp each of ground
cumin and paprika. Heat a griddle and cook
the chicken and vegetables for 15 minutes,
until cooked through. Serve with cooked rice
and some fat free natural yogurt mixed with
chopped coriander.

Mamma mia meatballs

breakfast
Continental breakfast

Serve slices of cooked turkey, wafer thin ham and 35g thinly sliced Edam cheese (a) with halved baby plum tomatoes and a 60g wholemeal roll (b).

lunch
Green eggs & ham

In a large pan, gently cook a large bag of spinach until wilted. Meanwhile, cook a lean gammon steak in low calorie cooking spray for 5-10 minutes, depending on thickness. Alongside the gammon, cook a fried egg or 2. Serve the eggs with the spinach and gammon.

dinner
Spaghetti with meatballs

Mix extra lean minced beef with crushed garlic, fennel seeds, ground cumin and ground coriander and season well. Cover and chill for an hour. Place onion, garlic, carrot and celery in a pan with a can of chopped tomatoes and bring to the boil. Cover and simmer gently for 25-30 minutes, stirring occasionally. Season well and blitz until smooth. Shape the mince into balls and stir-fry them for 2-3 minutes, in a frying pan sprayed with low calorie cooking spray, or until browned. Add the meatballs to the sauce and simmer gently for 8-10 minutes. Serve with cooked spaghetti and a crunchy green salad. Garnish with chopped parsley. Follow with an apple and a pear.

pasta and pie

breakfast
Bacon sandwich

Fill 2 slices of wholemeal bread (b) with lots of grilled lean bacon and tomato slices. Follow with wedges of melon.

lunch
Apple pasta salad

Mix cooled boiled pasta with diced apple, red onion, sweetcorn, tarragon, halved cherry tomatoes and lemon juice, and serve with lean cooked sliced meats. Have a big fresh fruit salad for afters.

dinner
Shepherd's pie

Place lean lamb chunks in a food processor and blend until it resembles mince. Cook the mince with carrot, onion, celery and canned chopped tomatoes, and top with mashed swede and potato. Bake in the oven at 200°C/Gas 6 for 15-20 minutes. Serve with carrots, broccoli and cauliflower. Finish with a large bunch of grapes.

cut the mustard

breakfast
Cooked breakfast

Grill Quorn Best Ever Sausages (1 Syn each) and serve with baked beans, scrambled eggs and mushrooms fried in low calorie cooking spray. Serve with 2 slices of wholemeal toast (b).

lunch
Chicken & corn chowder

Gently cook a large chopped onion in a little vegetable stock for 10 minutes to soften. Add a large chopped potato and a drained can of sweetcorn. Cover with stock and cook until the potato is tender. Blitz half the soup and mix together with the chunkier soup. Add cooked skinless shredded chicken and heat through.

dinner
Mustard pork chops

Soften a couple of thinly sliced onions in a non-stick frying pan sprayed with low calorie cooking spray, and transfer to a bowl. Brown lean pork chops in an ovenproof frying pan. Mix the onions with a little Dijon mustard (½ Syn per level tsp) and a few spoonfuls of fat free French dressing. Pour over the pork and grill on a medium-high heat for 10-15 minutes, turning until the pork chops are cooked through. Serve with cooked new potatoes, carrots and broccoli. Enjoy slices of fresh pineapple for afters.

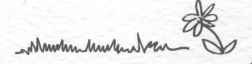

Rigatoni alla amatriciana, pg 74

eating in: the new eating out

Crazy about curry?
Passionate about pizza?
Hungry for a hot dog?

Now you can enjoy all your favourite eating out meals in – and save Syns! Whether it's supper for one, a romantic meal for two or a delicious dinner party for friends and family, you'll find whatever you fancy – and more – right here!

galloping gourmet

breakfast

Full English breakfast

Grill lots of lean bacon and serve with grilled tomatoes and mushrooms, baked beans, a fried egg (or 2) and potato cubes both cooked in low calorie cooking spray. Serve with 2 slices of wholemeal toast (b).

lunch

Veggie rice stir-fry

Stir-fry cooked rice with sliced red onion, mixed peppers, celery, mushrooms, Quorn pieces, mangetout and soy sauce. Follow with choco-nana pudding: stir Options chocolate powder (2 Syns per 11g sachet) and sliced banana into a pot of Total 0% Fat Greek Yogurt.

dinner

Roast gammon with hot & fruity salsa

Serve slices of lean roast gammon with salsa (diced mango, chopped red chilli, chopped coriander and lime juice), new potatoes and lots of mangetout.

seafood and eat it

breakfast

Weetabix & crackerbread

Have 30g Weetabix Wholegrain Minis (b) with milk (a) and some chopped berries.

lunch

Chicken & caramelised onions

Thinly slice 2 onions and cook, covered, in a pan sprayed with low calorie cooking spray, until soft. Add a teaspoon of sweetener and turn up the heat to caramelise. Slice open some chicken breast fillets horizontally and open out like a book. Spinkle with seasoning and cook under a hot grill or on a hot griddle. Serve on crisp lettuce leaves and top with the browned onions.

dinner

Prawn egg fried rice

Stir-fry some finely chopped garlic, root ginger, spring onions and red chilli for a couple of minutes in a large non-stick frying pan sprayed with low calorie cooking spray. Add cooked basmati rice, some defrosted peas and some cooked and peeled prawns. Make a well in the middle and add a beaten egg, stirring to scramble. When cooked through, mix into the rice.

the pizza resistance

breakfast

Gammon & eggs

Cook scrambled eggs with a good pinch of dried chilli flakes. Serve with a griddled lean gammon steak and follow with a piece of fruit or two.

lunch

Mushroom 'pizzas'

Roast large field mushrooms at 200°C/Gas 6 for 20 minutes. Spoon on canned chopped tomatoes with onions and garlic and arrange some wafer thin ham on top. Place back in the oven for about 10 minutes until heated through. Serve with a bag of mixed leaves and some cooked green beans thrown in. Follow with a Slimming World Hi-fi Bar, any variety (b).

dinner

Chicken & vegetable curry

Cook a large chopped onion in low calorie cooking spray until soft, add a little grated ginger, garlic and a tbsp of curry powder. Add chicken stock and cubed skinless chicken breast fillets. Cook for 20 minutes, adding a selection of vegetables half way through, eg spinach leaves, carrot matchsticks, small cauliflower florets, halved green beans. Serve with cooked rice.

mango madness

breakfast

Eggs Benedict

Top 2 slices of wholemeal toast (b) with sliced lean ham, wilted spinach and a poached egg or two. Drizzle over a sauce of warmed fat free natural fromage frais mixed with chopped tarragon and seasoning.

lunch

Chicken & mango salsa rice

Mix cooked rice with torn cooked skinless chicken fillets and sliced sugar snap peas. Make a salsa by mixing ripe diced mango with finely chopped red onion, red chilli and cucumber. Stir some coriander leaves and baby spinach leaves into the rice and top each serving with a spoonful of salsa.

dinner

Soy beef & noodles

Fry thinly sliced lean sirloin beef pieces in a large wok sprayed with low calorie cooking spray. Remove them and add a bag of sliced spring greens to the pan with a little water, cover and cook for a few minutes to wilt. Add a liberal amount of light soy sauce and mix with the beef and some boiled noodles.

steak out

breakfast

Honey nut strawberries

30g Nestlé Honey Nut Shredded Wheat
(b) with milk (a) followed by some fresh
strawberries topped with Strawberry
Müllerlight Yogurt.

lunch

Tomato pasta in a flash

Cook a whole punnet of cherry tomatoes in
a non-stick frying pan until the skins burst,
add some green beans and asparagus
with a spoonful of water and cook for a few
minutes. Serve with cooked pasta shapes.
Enjoy a bunch of grapes for afters.

dinner

Steak & Slimming World chips

Grill a lean steak to your liking and serve with
Slimming World chips (see recipe on page
54) and a selection of vegetables. Follow
with sliced banana smothered in Müllerlight
Banana & Custard Yogurt.

Chicken & seafood paella, opposite

fiesta feast

breakfast

Baked tomato & eggs

Heat 2 cans of chopped tomatoes in a saucepan and reduce over a medium-high heat for 10 minutes. Add a crushed garlic clove, chopped jalapeno pepper and seasoning. Pour into a large ovenproof dish and make 3-4 small wells in the sauce to break the eggs into. Bake in a preheated oven at 190°C/Gas 5 until the eggs are set.

lunch

Ham & lentil soup

Cook lean gammon, chopped onions, canned green lentils and diced carrots in stock until the gammon and lentils are tender. Serve with a 60g wholemeal roll (b). Follow with apples and pears for pud.

dinner

Chicken & seafood paella

Sauté finely chopped onions in low calorie cooking spray for 4-5 minutes. Add garlic, peppers and carrots, and continue to sauté for a few minutes. Add paella rice, a bay leaf and a pinch of saffron threads to the pan. Stir in chicken stock, bring to a simmer and cook, uncovered, over a gentle heat for 15 minutes. Add raw tiger prawns, live mussels, cooked shredded chicken and fresh or frozen peas, cover tightly and turn the heat to very low. Allow to cook for another 12-15 minutes until all the liquid is absorbed. Remove from the heat and leave to stand, covered, for 10 minutes. Stir in chopped parsley and garnish with lemon wedges. Finish with summer fruits layered in a glass with fat free natural yogurt.

French fancies

breakfast

Cinnamon French toast with banana

Beat an egg in a shallow bowl and dip 2 slices of halved wholemeal bread (b). Cook in a non-stick frying pan with a sprinkling of ground cinnamon on each side and serve with thinly sliced banana.

lunch

Fruity jacket

Top a large jacket potato with lots of low fat natural cottage cheese mixed with chunks of fresh peach and pineapple, and serve with a crisp mixed salad.

dinner

Chicken & pea risotto

Enjoy a generous serving of chicken & pea risotto (see recipe on page 72) and follow with a couple of satsumas.

Haddock & peppers, opposite

tikka look at this!

breakfast

Citrus kick

Have a large bowl of fresh orange
and grapefruit segments, followed by
your favourite Free Müllerlight Yogurt.

lunch

Chicken tikka sandwich

Mix chunks of cooked skinless chicken
with fat free natural fromage frais flavoured
to taste with tikka curry powder, and pile
on to 2 slices of wholemeal bread (b).
Serve with a crisp mixed salad.

dinner

Haddock & peppers

Roast pepper halves in a preheated oven
at 190°C/Gas 5 for 15 minutes. Wilt a bag
of spinach with a little crushed garlic in a
large pan for 2 minutes. Mix quark, basil and
mustard (½ Syn per level tsp) with some
seasoning and spread over haddock fillets.
Arrange sliced tomatoes on top and place
on a baking tray lined with baking parchment.
Fill the peppers with the spinach and cover
with foil. Place back in the oven along with
the tray of haddock. Cook for 20-25 minutes
(depending on the thickness of the fish).
Serve the fish with the pepper halves and
some new potatoes if desired.

chicken and pea risotto

Ready in 35 minutes

Serves 4

Free on Extra Easy

1 large onion, chopped

1 celery stick, finely chopped

1 leek, finely chopped

low calorie cooking spray

275g dried risotto rice

1.1 litres chicken stock

225g frozen peas

275g cooked chicken, shredded

1. In a deep frying pan, cook the onion, celery and leek in low calorie cooking spray for 15 minutes to soften. Add the risotto rice and stir in.

2. Heat the chicken stock in a saucepan and gradually add the hot stock to the rice, stirring between each addition until the rice absorbs the liquid. Add the frozen peas after 10 minutes and continue to cook until the rice grains are cooked. This will take about 18-20 minutes.

3. Stir in the cooked chicken towards the end to heat through.

4. Serve with a large mixed salad.

strawberry ice forever

breakfast

Ham omelette

Make a ham omelette and serve with baked beans and 2 slices of wholemeal toast (b). Follow with a 120g pot Danone Shape Delights 0% Yogurt, any variety (½ Syn).

lunch

Chicken couscous salad

Prepare couscous according to the packet instructions and mix with cooked skinless chicken chunks, sliced cucumber, radishes, spring onions, orange segments and chopped fresh mixed herbs. Drizzle with fat free vinaigrette. Follow with fresh cherries for dessert.

dinner

Rigatoni alla amatriciana

Stir-fry lean bacon, onion, carrot, celery, garlic and dried red chillies (to taste) for 2-3 minutes over a medium heat. Add canned chopped tomatoes and sweetener, and bring to the boil. Stir in chopped basil. Reduce the heat, cover and cook on very low for 20-25 minutes, stirring occasionally. Season well. Toss the sauce through cooked rigatoni pasta and serve garnished with basil leaves. Follow with strawberry ice: stir some chopped strawberries into a Müllerlight Strawberry Yogurt, place in a mould and freeze until set.

peri-perfection

breakfast

Brunch potatoes & beans

Chop cooked new potatoes, spray with low calorie cooking spray and cook in a preheated oven at 190°C/Gas 5 for 20 minutes. Serve with baked beans, grilled mushrooms and tomatoes.

lunch

Hot dog & onions

Cook sliced onion in low calorie cooking spray until soft. Cook Quorn Best Ever Sausages (1 Syn each) and serve in 60g wholemeal rolls (b) with the onions and a side salad and a drizzle of tomato ketchup (1 Syn per level tbsp).

dinner

Peri-peri chicken jacket

Marinate chicken breast fillets in peri-peri marinade (1 Syn per level tbsp) for 15 minutes and cook under a hot grill or on a hot griddle. Serve with a jacket potato and a salad of bottled roasted peppers, sliced tomatoes and mixed leaves.

Butternut squash stew, pg 78

accelerate your
success

Speed your way to weight loss without ever going hungry…

Power packed with health-boosting foods, these satisfying menus focus on Speed Foods, those foods that are especially slimmer-friendly, and promise to leave you smiling at the scales.

super free... super fast

breakfast

Sssausages!

Grill some Quorn Best Ever Sausages
(1 Syn each) and serve with poached eggs
and canned plum tomatoes.

lunch

Celery & cucumber salad with smoked fish

Mix finely sliced celery with sliced cucumber
and salad cress. Add lemon juice and
seasoning and serve with a bag of mixed
leaves and some smoked trout or drained
tuna in spring water. Serve with a 60g
wholemeal roll (b).

dinner

Butternut squash stew

In a large casserole dish, mix diced butternut
squash, drained butter beans, button
mushrooms, fresh chopped tomatoes and
chopped thyme. Add 1 tbsp of cold water
to cornflour (3½ Syns per level tbsp) and
mix well. Add to hot vegetable stock and
pour over the vegetables. Season, cover and
cook in a preheated oven at 200°C/Gas 6
for 45 minutes, or until the butternut squash
is tender. Prepare couscous according to
packet instructions, then stir in thinly sliced
spring onions, lemon juice and seasoning.
Serve the stew with the couscous, a sprinkle
of fresh parsley and wedge of fresh lemon.

natural goodness

breakfast

Fruity melon boat

Pile a melon boat high with fresh pineapple chunks, raspberries and Total 0% Fat Greek Yogurt. Follow with 2 slices of wholemeal toast (b) topped with poached eggs.

lunch

Tuna & sweetcorn jacket

Top a jacket potato with lots of tuna and sweetcorn mixed together with extra light mayonnaise (1 Syn per level tbsp) and black pepper. Serve with lots of mixed salad.

dinner

Chicken breasts & salsa

Slice chicken breast fillets into strips and marinate in the juice of a lemon for 10 minutes. Sprinkle with salt and griddle for about 15 minutes, turning until cooked through. Make a peach salsa by mixing chopped ripe peaches with very finely chopped red onion and chopped chilli. Serve with cooked rice and vegetables of your choice.

today's just peachy

breakfast

Peachy Jordans

Have 35g Jordans Natural No Added Sugar Muesli (b) topped with sliced peaches and milk (a).

lunch

Broccoli, carrot & parsley salad with kidney beans

Lightly cook broccoli florets and drain. Coarsely grate carrots and mix with canned drained kidney beans, the cooked broccoli and plenty of parsley and seasoning.

dinner

Baked herby cod with watercress & green bean salad

Serve up a portion of baked herby cod (see recipe on page 82) and follow with a 125g pot of Ambrosia Rice Pudding (6½ Syns).

Turkey stir-fry with noodles, opposite

over the rainbow...

breakfast

Tropical fruit platter

Make up a platter of fresh prepared fruits like mango slices, star fruit, watermelon and pineapple and help yourself. Serve with 2 slices of wholemeal toast (b) topped with chocolate spread (1½ Syns per level tsp).

lunch

Rainbow rice salad

Mix cooked rice with chopped red onion, celery, radishes, cucumber, tomatoes, sweetcorn, mixed peppers and chopped fresh mint. Serve with a fat free salad dressing of your choice.

dinner

Turkey stir-fry with noodles

Stir-fry strips of skinless turkey breast with spring onion, garlic, red pepper, baby sweetcorn, green beans, soy sauce and Chinese 5-spice powder and serve with boiled noodles. Enjoy a few plums for afters.

baked **herby cod** with **watercress** and **green bean salad**

Ready in 35 minutes

Serves 4

Free on Extra Easy

800g large new potatoes,
peeled and cut into 1cm pieces

6 spring onions, thickly sliced

1 tbsp each of chopped dill
and coriander, plus extra to serve

4 x 150g skinless and
boneless cod fillets

juice of 2 limes,
plus extra wedges to serve

salt and freshly ground black pepper

200g fine green beans, halved

85g bag watercress

10 white seedless grapes, halved

75g radishes, thinly sliced

1. Preheat the oven to 220°C/Gas 7. Boil the potatoes in lightly salted water for 10 minutes and drain. Transfer to a large ovenproof dish and sprinkle over the spring onions and herbs. Mix well.

2. Place the cod fillets on top, drizzle over the lime juice and season well. Bake in the oven for 20 minutes.

3. Cook the green beans in lightly salted boiling water for 3 minutes. Drain and cool under cold running water.

4. Assemble the salad in a large bowl. Layer the watercress and then scatter over the green beans, grapes and radishes.

5. Scatter the extra herbs over the fish and serve with the potatoes, the watercress salad and lime wedges.

laying down the slaw!

breakfast

Fruitibix

Two Weetabix (b) topped with lots of mixed berries and milk (a).

lunch

Cod & corn coleslaw

Mix together thinly shredded cabbage, grated carrot, drained sweetcorn, chopped red and green peppers, thinly sliced celery and spring onions. Stir in some fat free French dressing and serve with a grilled or poached cod fillet.

dinner

Roast chicken dinner

Roast skinless chicken breast and all the trimmings: dry roast potatoes and parsnips, cauliflower, carrots and peas. Serve with gravy (1½ Syns per 100ml). Follow with a Toffee apple pudding: stir some chopped apple into a pot of Müllerlight Toffee Yogurt.

make room for mushrooms

breakfast

Tricolore baked beans & egg

In a non-stick pan, gently sweat half a chopped small onion, a handful of chopped peppers and mushrooms until soft. Add half a can of baked beans and cook to combine. Serve with a poached egg.

lunch

Roasted mushroom soup

Roast eight large mushrooms in a preheated oven at 200°C/Gas 6 for 30 minutes until really soft. Transfer to a blender and blitz, gradually adding hot vegetable stock until you have the desired consistency. Season to taste. Reheat if necessary and serve scattered with some herbs. Serve with a 60g wholemeal roll (b).

dinner

Spanish-style prawn & haddock chickpeas

Cook a chopped red onion in low calorie cooking spray until soft and add some crushed garlic. Tip in a can of tomatoes, a can of drained chickpeas and a little fish stock. Cook for 10 minutes. Add cubed skinned pieces of haddock and large, raw peeled prawns, cover and cook until the fish is cooked and hot all the way through. Serve with green vegetables.

zest for life

breakfast

Citrus start

Cut two halves of grapefruit into segments and chill in the fridge overnight. Sprinkle over sweetener the next morning and serve with blueberries. Follow with a Healthy Extra portion of cereal (b) served with milk (a).

lunch

Tomato & mixed bean soup

Place onion, garlic, celery and carrot in a pan along with vegetable stock, canned chopped tomatoes and sweetener. Bring to the boil. Reduce the heat to medium, and cook for 15-20 minutes. Add green beans and canned drained mixed beans and cook for a further 10 minutes. Season well. Garnish with a swirl of fat free natural fromage frais and sprinkle over chopped chives. Have a fresh fruit salad topped with fat free natural yogurt for dessert.

dinner

Oriental cod

Place a cod steak in tin foil with chopped spring onions, soy sauce and fresh chopped ginger, and bake in a preheated oven at 180°C/Gas 4 for 20-30 minutes. Serve with cooked noodles, Oriental vegetables and extra soy sauce to taste.

magic **mussels**

breakfast

Beans on toast

Smother 2 slices of wholemeal toast (b) with baked beans and follow with fresh raspberries topped with fat free natural yogurt.

lunch

Carrot, couscous & orange salad

Mix grated carrots with cooked couscous, orange slices, the juice of ½ orange (½ Syn) and ½ tsp cumin seeds. Serve with deli turkey slices and lots of fresh watercress. Grab a bunch of grapes for afters.

dinner

Garlic mussels with tagliatelle

Finely chop three shallots and cook gently with some garlic and finely chopped tomatoes. Add a kilo bag of cleaned mussels with 200ml of fish stock and cook them with a lid on until all the mussels have opened, discarding any that remain closed. Mix in cooked tagliatelle, the juice of a lemon and chopped parsley.

Tomato & mixed bean soup, opposite

be good to yourself

breakfast

Full English & cereal

Grill lean bacon and serve with tomatoes, mushrooms and an egg fried in low calorie cooking spray. Enjoy 35g Nestlé Bitesize Shredded Wheat (b) with milk (a) and raspberries while it's cooking.

lunch

Sweet baked potato

Bake a sweet potato at 190°C/Gas 5 for 45 minutes and fill with lots of baked beans. Serve with a large salad. Follow with some kiwi fruit and grapes.

dinner

Tomato & basil fish parcels

Slice a tomato per serving. On a large foil square, place half the sliced tomato and top with a skinless and boneless white fish fillet. Season lightly and arrange the remaining tomato on top with some finely chopped spring onions. Tear plenty of basil over and seal the parcel. Cook on a baking tray in a preheated oven at 190°C/Gas 5 for 20-30 minutes. Serve with lots of Superfree veg.

Turkey steak wraps, opposite

wrap it up!

breakfast

Brunch omelette with leeks

Cook very finely sliced leek in 2 tbsp of water until soft. Mix with 1 large egg yolk, 2 tbsp of quark and 1 tbsp of chopped parsley. Whisk the large egg white until stiff and fold into the yolk mixture. Spray a small non-stick frying pan with low calorie cooking spray and pour in the egg mixture. Cook until set and finish under the grill.

lunch

Italian pasta salad

Mix cooked pasta shapes with drained tuna in brine, canned drained borlotti beans, chopped apple and red onion. Drizzle with fat free vinaigrette and serve with a green salad.

Follow with 375g stewed apple (b) topped with some fat free natural fromage frais.

dinner

Turkey steak wraps

Make a cut down the side of a turkey steak and fill with a mixture of quark, garlic and spring onion. Season each steak, top with basil leaves and wrap in Parma ham (½ Syn per slice). Bake in a preheated oven at 200°C/ Gas 6 for 30 minutes. Serve with carrots, green beans and baby sweetcorn.

going global

Cook your way around the world!

The next few pages are brimming with international inspiration so prepare to take your tastebuds to places they've never been before! From America to Europe to the Far East, these menu planners are inspired by exciting flavours and ingredients and you don't have to be a world-class chef to cook them!

Chinese pork stir-fry, pg 103

Cajun creation

breakfast

Mushroom omelette

Make a large mixed mushroom omelette and serve with baked beans. Finish with 2 slices of wholemeal toast (b) spread with jam or marmalade (½ Syn per level tsp).

lunch

Cajun-style veg kebabs

Alternately thread cubed vegetables, such as red onions, red and yellow peppers and courgettes, onto pre-soaked bamboo skewers. Mix some Cajun seasoning and lemon juice together and brush all over. Place under a hot grill until cooked through, turning regularly. Serve with cooked rice, adding a tsp of turmeric to the water as it cooks.

dinner

Cajun chicken burgers with spicy wedges

Sprinkle potato wedges with Cajun spice mix and bake in a preheated oven at 200°C/Gas 6 for 25-30 minutes. Make the burgers by placing lean chicken chunks in a food processor with spring onion, red pepper, garlic, ginger, flat-leaf parsley, Cajun spice mix and seasoning. Blend until the mixture resembles mince and divide into burgers. Spray with low calorie cooking spray and cook under a hot grill for 5-6 minutes or until cooked through. Serve with the wedges, a tomato and onion salsa and a crisp green salad. For dessert, have some fresh pineapple slices.

the spice is right!

breakfast

Something fishy

Grill kippers and serve with grilled tomatoes, scrambled egg and 2 slices of wholemeal toast (b).

lunch

Indian chicken salad

Rub a skinless chicken breast with ground cumin and lime juice and cook on a hot griddle for a few minutes each side until cooked through. Remove and slice thinly. Mix with thinly sliced red onion, carrot matchsticks and some thinly sliced courgettes and radishes. Finish with a sprinkling of fresh coriander. Have some quartered fresh oranges for pud.

dinner

Beef curry and rice

Enjoy a portion of beef curry and rice (see recipe on next page). Round off the meal with a bowl of mixed berries smothered in fat free natural fromage frais.

Cajun chicken burgers with spicy wedges, opposite

beef curry and rice

Ready in 50 minutes

Serves 4

Free on Extra Easy

1 red onion, sliced

low calorie cooking spray

500g lean rump steak

1 red pepper, deseeded and chopped

1 tbsp madras curry powder

2 tbsp tomato purée

1 medium butternut squash

250g mushrooms, halved

275ml beef stock

200g dried basmati rice

150g fat free natural yogurt

freshly chopped coriander

1. Cook the onion in low calorie cooking spray for 10 minutes. Cut the steak into strips, add to the pan with the red pepper and cook, stirring, for 3 minutes. Add the curry powder and tomato purée and mix well.

2. Peel, deseed and chop the squash and stir into the pan with the mushrooms. Pour in the stock and bring to the boil. Cover and cook for 25 minutes.

3. Meanwhile, cook the rice in lightly salted boiling water for 10 minutes and drain.

4. Serve the curry drizzled with yogurt, scattered with coriander and the rice on the side.

Bella Italia!

breakfast

Bacon, mushrooms & tomatoes

Lots of grilled lean bacon, poached mushrooms and grilled vine tomatoes.

lunch

Rice & peas

Place onions, carrots, celery and garlic in a saucepan. Add stock and rice, bring to the boil and simmer very gently for 15-20 minutes. Stir in frozen peas and cook for 5 minutes, add chopped parsley and season well.

dinner

Ham & egg linguine

Cook pasta according to the packet instructions. Drain well. Toss the pasta with grated Parmesan cheese (1½ Syns per level tbsp), chopped parsley and seasoning. Stir in lean diced ham and top with an egg fried in low calorie cooking spray. Follow with 450g stewed fresh apricots (b) topped with fat free natural fromage frais for pud.

Spanish slim-spiration

breakfast

Spanish tomato bread

Toast 2 slices of wholemeal bread (b),
rub one of the sides with a cut garlic clove.
Halve a very ripe tomato and rub the cut
side onto the same side of toast, discard
the skin. Top with sliced lean ham and serve.

lunch

Spanish omelette

Mix thickly sliced potatoes with chopped
onion, beaten eggs, chopped parsley and
seasoning. Cook in low calorie cooking spray
until set, then place under a preheated hot grill
until golden. Serve with baked beans and a
crisp mixed salad. Enjoy fresh pineapple slices
dipped into fat free natural yogurt for dessert.

dinner

Spanish rice with prawns

Spray a pan with low calorie cooking spray
and cook a chopped onion and red pepper
until soft. Stir in 150g paella rice with 400ml
chicken stock and sprinkle with saffron.
Cover and cook for 20 minutes until the rice
is tender. Add 110g cooked and peeled
prawns and heat through.

Eastern promise

breakfast

Bran & berries

Have 40g Kellogg's All-Bran (b) with milk (a) and top with mixed berries.

lunch

Oriental chicken couscous salad

Mix cooked couscous with chopped cooked skinless chicken breast, red peppers, spring onions and cucumber. Make a delicious Oriental dressing by mixing a squeeze of lime juice with honey (1 Syn per level tsp), some freshly grated root ginger and a dash of soy sauce. Choose a Free Müllerlight Yogurt for pud.

dinner

Roasted oriental pollack

Place pollack fillets in a baking dish and top with shredded ginger, light soy sauce, star anise and chilli sauce (½ Syn per level tbsp). Add red chillies and spring onion, cover with foil and bake in a preheated oven at 200°C/ Gas 6 for 8-10 minutes. Boil some rice and set aside. Spray a frying pan with low calorie cooking spray and place over a high heat. Add spring onion, halved baby sweetcorn and mangetout, carrot, red pepper, ground ginger and bean sprouts. Stir-fry for 6-8 minutes, add rice and dark soy sauce and stir-fry for a further 3-4 minutes. Serve with the fish.

fast French food

breakfast

Herby French omelette

Whisk 3 large eggs with tbsp of water,
1 heaped tbsp chives and flat-leaf parsley
with some seasoning. Cook in a small non-
stick frying pan, finishing off under a hot grill.

lunch

Ratatouille spud

Fill a jacket potato with a 390g can of Co-op,
Morrison's or Waitrose Ratatouille (1 Syn) and
serve with a generous mixed salad. Follow
with 300g apricots canned in juice (b) for pud.

dinner

Chicken chasseur

Enjoy a quick French supper: a 420g pack
Tesco Finest Classic Chicken Chasseur
(1 Syn) served with fluffy mashed potato and
lots of Free vegetables.

Roasted oriental pollack, opposite

la bamba

breakfast

Nice 'n' toasty

Spread 2 slices of wholemeal toast (b) with jam or marmalade (½ Syn per level tsp), and follow with a banana and a sachet of low calorie instant hot chocolate drink (2 Syns).

Mexican tuna topped jacket, opposite

lunch

Chilled gazpacho

Place chopped tomatoes, cucumber, spring onions, red and green pepper and garlic in a food processor. Add fresh basil and blend until smooth. Serve chilled. Follow with lots of fresh pineapple chunks and a Müllerlight Vanilla Yogurt.

dinner

Viva España garlic prawns

Place raw king prawns in an ovenproof dish with thinly sliced garlic cloves and a large pinch of dried chilli flakes. Squeeze over the juice of a lemon and bake in the oven at 200°C/Gas 6, until cooked through, about 12-15 minutes. Serve with rice and green vegetables. Follow with sliced oranges.

Mexican twist

breakfast

Heuvos rancheros

Dice 12 lean bacon rashers and fry in low calorie cooking spray for 10-12 minutes with a chopped onion, 2 crushed garlic cloves and a chopped red pepper. Add 2 cans of chopped tomatoes, a little sweetener and ground cumin and a pinch of chilli flakes. Simmer for 45 minutes until reduced. Transfer to an ovenproof dish and make four hollows. Break an egg into each hollow and bake in a preheated oven at 200°C/Gas 6 for 20-25 minutes.

lunch

Mexican tuna topped jacket

Mix together some drained kidney beans, drained tuna in brine and drained sweetcorn in a bowl. Add thinly sliced red pepper, diced spring onion, lemon juice, extra light mayonnaise (1 Syn per level tbsp), and a few drops of Tabasco sauce. Mix well and use to top a jacket potato and serve with a crisp green salad. Follow with 275g pears canned in juice (b), topped with fat free natural yogurt.

dinner

Mexican-style rice with vegetables

Fry some chopped onion, garlic and smoked paprika in low calorie cooking spray until soft and set aside. Cook some rice according to the packet instructions and for the last few minutes of cooking add some frozen mixed vegetables to the pan. Bring back to the boil until the rice and vegetables are cooked. Drain and stir through the onion mixture.

born in the USA

breakfast

Bacon brunch

Gently wilt a couple of handfuls of baby leaf spinach and place on the middle of a plate. Top with a soft poached egg and some grilled lean back bacon.

Chinese salmon noodle lunchbox salad, opposite

lunch

Pastrami salad sandwich

Fill 2 slices of wholemeal bread (b) with slices of lean pastrami and lots of mixed lettuce leaves, sliced cucumber and sliced pickled gherkins. Grab a few plums for afters.

dinner

Griddled chicken with couscous

Heat a griddle and cook a skinless chicken breast with slices of courgette, aubergine and peppers. Toss through cooked couscous with some chopped parsley and mint. Have any flavour Options Chocolate drink (11g sachet) mixed with natural fat free yogurt for pud.

eastern feast

breakfast

Fruity crunch

Serve 35g Kellog's All-Bran Bran Flakes (b) with milk (a) and top with fresh berries of your choice.

lunch

Chinese salmon noodle lunchbox salad

Sprinkle a salmon fillet with 5-spice mix and cook under a hot grill for 10-12 minutes or until cooked through. Set aside. Meanwhile, stir-fry red pepper, spring onions, mangetout, garlic, ginger, water chestnuts, baby sweetcorn and bean sprouts for 6-8 minutes. Add cooked egg noodles to the pan with soy sauce. Toss to mix well and stir fry for 1-2 minutes. Remove from the heat. Break the salmon fillets into bite-sized pieces and gently toss into the noodle mixture. Follow with some fresh lychees.

dinner

Chinese pork stir-fry

Place lean thin strips of pork in a shallow bowl and sprinkle with a little Chinese seasoning. Cook in a wok sprayed with low calorie cooking spray for 5 minutes. Add some carrot matchsticks, shredded cabbage, sliced mixed peppers, sliced mushrooms and bean sprouts. Cook for a further 3-4 minutes before serving with lime wedges.

Gammon &
pineapple, pg 108

BEST OF BRITISH

Nothing tastes better than traditional English fare – and Slimming World does it with a healthy twist!

From bacon and egg sandwiches to proper Sunday roasts, we've got the nation's favourite foods covered for breakfast, lunch and dinner – every day of the week. Fill up, slim down and feel great!

SOLDIER ON

breakfast

Boiled eggs & soldiers

Boil eggs to your liking and serve with soldiers made from 2 slices of wholemeal toast (b), follow with lots of sliced banana layered in a tall glass with a Müllerlight Toffee Yogurt.

lunch

Jubilee chicken salad

Marinate pieces of skinless chicken breast in lime juice, garlic and grated ginger. Grill until cooked through and leave to cool. Mix with cooked, cooled and quartered new potatoes and pour over a dressing of fat free natural fromage frais, extra light mayonnaise (1 Syn per level tbsp), lime juice and grated ginger. Sprinkle over chopped parsley and mix well. Serve on a bed of watercress.

dinner

Fish, chips & peas

Dip white fish fillets in beaten egg and then breadcrumbs (4½ Syns per 25g) mixed with chopped herbs. Bake in a preheated oven at 220°C/Gas 7 for 15-20 minutes. Serve with Slimming World chips (see recipe on page 54) and lots of mushy peas.

Fishy on a Dishy

breakfast

Creamy orchard medley

Top chunks of apple and pear with a pot of Total 0% Fat Greek Yogurt.

lunch

Sardines on toast

Top 2 slices of wholemeal toast (b) with plenty of sardines canned in tomato sauce. Serve with a big crunchy salad.

dinner

Pork chops

Grill some lean pork chops until cooked through and serve with new potatoes, mashed swede, green beans, gravy made with granules (1½ Syns per 100ml) and a dollop of apple sauce (1 Syn per level tbsp).

*Boiled eggs &
soldiers, opposite*

CHIPS GLORIOUS CHIPS

breakfast

Hot stuff

35g Nestlé Bitesize Shredded Wheat (b) topped with hot milk (a) and sliced banana.

lunch

Egg, chips & beans

Top Slimming World chips (see recipe on page 54) with baked beans and an egg fried in low calorie cooking spray and serve with a green salad.

dinner

Gammon & pineapple

Grill a lean gammon steak to your liking, top with slices of fresh pineapple and serve with new potatoes, roasted vine tomatoes, baby sweetcorn and mangetout.

*Prawn marie rose
jacket potato, opposite*

Quintessentially English

breakfast

English summer berry treat

Mix strawberries, raspberries and blackberries or frozen fruits of the forest with a 120g pot of Danone Shape Delights 0% Yogurt, any variety (½ Syn), and 35g Post Grape Nuts (b).

lunch

Prawn marie rose jacket potato

Mix lots of cooked and peeled prawns with fat free natural fromage frais that has been flavoured with tomato ketchup (1 Syn per level tbsp) and use to top a jacket potato. Serve with a crunchy salad of mixed green leaves, halved cherry tomatoes and pepper strips.

dinner

Leg of lamb

Enjoy a generous serving of braised lamb with barley (see recipe on next page). Follow with a 175g pot of Hartley's Low Calorie Jelly (½ Syn).

WHOLE BRAISED LEG OF LAMB WITH BARLEY

Ready in 1 hour 10 minutes

Serves 4

Free on Extra Easy

low calorie cooking spray

1.25kg pack casserole vegetables, peeled and cut into large chunks

800g boneless lean half leg of lamb

salt and freshly ground black pepper

2 tomatoes, chopped

110g pearl barley

1 cinnamon stick

850ml lamb stock

a small handful of flat-leaf parsley, roughly chopped

1. Spray a very large saucepan with low calorie cooking spray and add the vegetables. Stir over a high heat for 5 minutes to soften.

2. Add the leg of lamb and brown all over. Season to taste.

3. Add the tomatoes, pearl barley, cinnamon stick and lamb stock to the pan and stir everything well. Cover and cook over a medium heat for 1 hour, until the meat is tender and the barley is cooked. Scatter over the parsley.

4. Transfer the lamb onto a chopping board and slice into large chunks. Serve the pearl barley and vegetables in a large shallow bowls with the meat arranged on top.

COOL AS A CUCUMBER

breakfast

Kippers & scrambled eggs

Grill plenty of kippers and serve with
scrambled egg.

lunch

Ham & cucumber sandwiches

Fill 2 slices of wholemeal bread (b) with plenty
of sliced lean ham and lots of sliced cucumber.
Cut into triangles and serve with iceberg
lettuce, grated carrot and sliced radishes.
Follow with an orange and some grapes.

dinner

Beef stew

Place whole shallots, sliced carrots and
chunks of lean braising steak in a large pan
and pour over enough water to cover. Stir
in tomato purée and a bouquet garni, cover
and simmer for 1½ hours. Add button
mushrooms and simmer for a further 20
minutes. Sprinkle over a stock cube or two
(to taste) and season. Serve with mashed
potatoes and broccoli.

Flying Start

breakfast

Full English breakfast

Grill lean bacon and sausages, Quorn
Best Ever (1 Syn each) and serve with grilled
tomatoes, mushrooms, baked beans and
eggs fried in low calorie cooking spray.

lunch

Leek & potato soup

Place chopped leeks, onion and potato in a
pan with vegetable or chicken stock and cook
until tender. Blend in a food processor and
season well. Sprinkle with nutmeg and serve
with a 60g crusty wholemeal roll (b).

dinner

Savoury mince & mashed potato

Cook extra lean minced beef with diced
carrots, onions and peas in low calorie
cooking spray. Serve with fluffy mashed
potatoes and cabbage. Top with gravy
made with granules (1½ Syns
per 100ml).

Beef stew, opposite

BIG AND BEEFY

breakfast

Bacon & egg 'toastie'

Fill 2 slices of wholemeal toast (b) with lots of grilled lean bacon, sliced tomato and an egg (or two) fried in low calorie cooking spray. Top with tomato ketchup or brown sauce (1 Syn per level tbsp), if wished.

lunch

Roast beef salad platter

Serve slices of lean roast beef (or roast chicken or ham) with radishes, beetroot, celery, round lettuce and new potatoes. Follow with wedges of melon and a Müllerlight Vanilla Yogurt.

dinner

Bubble & squeak cakes

Mash leftover potatoes and stir in leftover cabbage and some finely chopped onion. Season and mix well. Divide into individual cakes. Cook in a frying pan sprayed with low calorie cooking spray for 3-4 minutes each side until golden. Serve with mushy peas and baby carrots.

KING OF THE CASSEROLES

breakfast

Porridge & chopped fruit

Make up 35g plain porridge (b) with milk (a) and top with chunks of fresh peach, mango and pear.

lunch

'Quiche' & jacket

Season beaten eggs and pour into a frying pan, add diced onion and lots of chopped cooked lean bacon. Cook gently for 8-10 minutes until the bottom is set then finish off under a hot grill for 2-3 minutes. Serve with a jacket potato and a large mixed salad.

dinner

Steak & kidney casserole

Place chunks of lean stewing steak in a bowl with sliced lamb kidneys. Sprinkle over a little cornflour (3½ Syns per level tbsp), mustard powder and seasoning and toss to coat well. Transfer to a large saucepan with sliced onions and crushed garlic and fry for 5-6 minutes. Add beef stock, a bay leaf and chopped thyme, bring to the boil and cover and simmer for 1½ hours. Serve with new potatoes, green beans and broccoli.

BEANZ MEANZ SMILES

breakfast

Beans on toast

Top 2 slices of wholemeal toast (b) with plenty of baked beans and garnish with a flat-leaf parsley sprig. Follow with an apple.

lunch

Prawn cocktail

Top shredded iceberg lettuce with diced cucumber, halved cherry tomatoes, sliced pepper and celery, lots of cooked and peeled prawns and Kraft Light Thousand Island Dressing (1 Syn per level tbsp). Follow with some plums and satsumas.

dinner

Lancashire hotpot

Layer chunks of lean lamb, sliced carrot and onion in a casserole dish, sprinkle with thyme and top with thickly sliced potatoes. Pour some stock over the meat and vegetables to come just under the potato layer. Cover the dish and bake in a preheated oven at 180°C/Gas 4 for 2 hours. Uncover and bake for 30-35 minutes until the potatoes are crisp and golden. Serve with green beans and cauliflower.

Sunday Favourite

breakfast

Fresh fruit salad

Top a bowl of strawberries, raspberries and blackberries with a Müllerlight Vanilla Yogurt.

lunch

Proper roast dinner

Enjoy lots of lean roast beef served with mashed potatoes, dry-roast parsnips, carrots, cauliflower and peas, served with 1 small Yorkshire pudding (2½ Syns ready to heat) and topped with gravy made with granules (1½ Syns per 100ml).

tea

Egg & cress sandwiches

Mix chopped hard-boiled egg with extra light mayonnaise (1 Syn per level tbsp), spread onto 2 slices of wholemeal bread (b) and top with plenty of cress. Follow with a fresh fruit salad topped with fat free natural yogurt.

Beans on toast, opposite

*Grilled chicken
& mango salad,
pg 127*

prepare and go

You're only ever minutes away from a fabulously filling Food Optimising feast!

These tasty recipes are perfect when you're pushed for time and need to bust hunger fast. And some are ideal when you need to pack a snack to go or eat on the move too!

feeling *fruity?*

breakfast

Blueberry breakfast

Serve 35g Nestlé Bitesize Shredded Wheat (b) with milk (a) and top with blueberries.

lunch

Ham & fruity coleslaw

Mix together peeled and diced pear and apple with grated carrot and shredded white cabbage. Stir in fat free natural yogurt and finely grated lemon zest with seasoning. Serve with cooked lean ham.

dinner

Ratatouille baked spuds

Mix a can of chopped tomatoes with some chopped aubergine, courgette, peppers, onion and garlic. Cook gently for about 15 minutes. Serve on top of a jacket potato and accompany with a large mixed salad. Follow with a bowl of mixed berries topped with aerosol cream (2 Syns per 12.5g serving).

Chicken pasta salad, opposite

lean and mean

breakfast

Melon & strawberry yogurt 'trifle'

Layer finely chopped orange-fleshed melon
and strawberries in a plastic container
and top with fat free natural fromage frais.
Sprinkle over 35g Weetabix Crunchy Bran (b)
and breakfast on the move.

lunch

Chicken pasta salad

Add cooked skinless cubes of chicken to
cooked pasta along with spring onions, red
peppers and red onion. Toss to mix well.
Sprinkle with chopped tarragon and parsley.
Serve with fat free salad dressing on the
side. Follow with 1 Mr Kipling Lemon Slice
or French Fancy (5½ Syns each), and some
juicy satsumas.

dinner

Grilled lean lamb steaks with red pepper sauce

Chop onion and garlic and fry in low calorie
cooking spray. Add chopped red pepper,
a can of tomatoes and herbs, and simmer.
Pour over grilled lean lamb steaks and serve
with potatoes sautéed in low calorie cooking
spray, and green beans. Follow with some
fresh apricots.

crunch time

breakfast

Tropical fruit crunch

Layer chunks of kiwi fruit, pineapple and mango in a tall glass with 35g Kellogg's All-Bran (b) and fat free natural yogurt.

lunch

Tuna marinara pasta

Mix chopped cherry tomatoes, chopped capers and a handful of chopped flat-leaf parsley into cooked penne pasta with a can of drained tuna in spring water and mix well. Serve with a big side salad of cucumber and lettuce leaves.

dinner

Grilled gammon with Slimming World chips

Season lean gammon steaks and sprinkle over a little mustard powder. Spray with low calorie cooking spray, place under a medium-hot grill and cook for 4-5 minutes on each side. Serve with garden peas and Slimming World chips (see recipe on page 54) and a large salad. Have a Müllerlight Toffee Yogurt mixed with sliced banana for pud and round the meal off with a gin (4 Syns per 35ml) with slimline tonic.

tortilla thriller

breakfast

Banana crunch

Have 35g Post Grape Nuts (b) served with loads of sliced banana and milk (a).

lunch

Fresh tomato & basil soup

Cook chopped onions and fresh tomatoes in a saucepan for 5-10 minutes. Add stock and a carton of passata and heat through. Sieve to remove the skin and pips, then liquidise until smooth. Return to the pan, stir in chopped basil, season well and heat through.

dinner

Butternut squash tortilla

Have a generous serving of butternut squash tortilla (see recipe on next page) and follow with a Free Müllerlight Yogurt for dessert.

Grilled gammon with Slimming World chips, opposite

butternut squash tortilla

Ready in 50 minutes

Serves 4

Free on Extra Easy

400g butternut squash, cut into
bite-sized pieces (prepared weight)

400g new potatoes, cut into bite-sized
pieces

2 onions, thinly sliced

low calorie cooking spray

150g quark

6 large eggs, beaten

25g chives, chopped

salt and freshly ground black pepper

1. Boil the squash and potatoes in a large saucepan
   of lightly salted boiling water for 20 minutes.
   Drain well.

2. Cook the onions in low calorie cooking spray for
   15 minutes. Preheat the oven to 180°C/Gas 4.

3. In a large mixing bowl, beat the quark and
   gradually whisk in the eggs. Add the onions,
   squash, potatoes and half the chives with some
   seasoning and mix together well.

4. Heat a non-stick 26cm ovenproof frying pan
   sprayed with low calorie cooking spray. Spoon
   in the egg mixture and cook in the oven for
   25-30 minutes.

5. Transfer the tortilla to a plate and then scatter
   the remaining chives over. Leave to cool and
   then slice into portions. Pack in an airtight plastic
   container and serve with a big mixed salad.

a dish for all seasons

breakfast

Bananabix

Enjoy two Weetabix (b) and milk (a) topped with sliced banana and followed by a pear.

lunch

Tuna & mixed bean salad

In a large bowl, mix blanched green beans, halved cherry tomatoes, red onion, drained tuna in spring water, drained mixed beans and rocket leaves. Season and drizzle over fat free vinaigrette.

dinner

Salt & pepper chicken

Mix small skinless chicken fillets with dried mint, lemon juice, coarse sea salt and freshly ground black pepper and marinate for 10 minutes. Cook the chicken under a hot grill, turning to cook evenly, and serve with new potatoes and salad.

warm the cockles

breakfast

Simply bran flakes

Have 35g bran flakes (b) with milk (a) and follow with a big bunch of grapes.

lunch

Grilled chicken & mango salad

Place skinless chicken chunks in a shallow bowl. Dust with smoked paprika, drizzle with lemon juice and mix together well. Cook the chicken under a hot grill until cooked through. Leave to cool. Place in a bowl with some shredded white cabbage, grated carrot, sliced red onion and white wine vinegar and toss to mix well. Pour over a dressing of grated mango, chopped coriander, lime juice and seasoning. Have slices of pineapple for afters.

dinner

Quick spaghetti vongole

Cook spaghetti in a large pan of lightly salted boiling water. Meanwhile, cook crushed garlic with a couple of large pinches of chilli flakes in low calorie cooking spray and some chopped tomato flesh. Drain the spaghetti and add to the sauce with a jar of drained cooked cockles and a large handful of chopped parsley. Mix well and serve with a mixed salad.

spiced up steak

breakfast

Toast & fruit

Two slices of wholemeal toast (b) topped with jam or marmalade (½ Syn per level tsp). Finish off with lots of fresh grapefruit and orange segments.

lunch

Couscous ham salad

Mix couscous with cucumber, cherry tomatoes, red onion, strips of lean ham, black pepper, lemon juice and chopped coriander. Follow with some fresh strawberries topped with fat free natural yogurt.

dinner

Peppercorn steak

Sprinkle mustard powder over lean steaks and cook on a hot griddle. Serve with minted new potatoes, griddled tomato halves and peppercorn sauce (chopped onion, crushed garlic, beef stock, crushed pink peppercorns and Worcestershire sauce, heated until thickened and reduced. Remove from the heat and stir in fat free natural fromage frais).

flash in the pan

breakfast

Fruity wheats

35g Kellogg's Raisin Wheats (b) and milk (a) topped with sliced peaches and nectarines.

lunch

Turkey & rice salad

Mix some cooked shredded turkey and cooked rice with sliced mushrooms and drizzle with lemon juice. Serve with fresh basil and a mixed salad. Grab some blueberries and grapes for pud.

dinner

Roasted salmon with one-pan roasted veg

In a large roasting tin, roast cauliflower florets, new potatoes cut into small pieces, red pepper and red onion for 40 minutes in a preheated oven at 200°C/Gas 6. Add salmon fillets, each wrapped in a piece of Parma ham (½ Syn per slice), to the roasting vegetables half way through.

bellissimo!

breakfast

Bacon & eggs

Enjoy scrambled eggs served with grilled lean bacon, baked beans and mushrooms.

lunch

Ham salad sandwich

Fill 2 slices of wholemeal bread (b) with lean sliced ham, cucumber, lettuce, tomato and red onion. Accompany with a 22g bag Walkers French Fries (4½ Syns). Grab an apple and a pear for afters.

dinner

Italian-style chicken kebabs with pasta

In a small bowl, mix cubed skinless chicken with balsamic vinegar, mixed dried herbs and a crushed garlic clove. Thread onto skewers with cherry tomatoes, cubed courgette and large pieces of pepper. Cook under a hot grill, turning until cooked through. Serve with pasta that has been cooked with some frozen mixed vegetables.

use your noodle

breakfast

Apple porridge oats

Make up 35g plain porridge oats (b) with water and serve with a grated apple stirred through with a little fat free natural yogurt. Follow with a banana.

lunch

Smooth vegetable soup

In a large pan, mix equal quantities of onion, broccoli, cauliflower and peeled diced potatoes. Cover with hot vegetable stock and add some seasoning. Bring to the boil, lower to a simmer and cook for 25 minutes. Blitz until smooth and check the seasoning.

dinner

Pork & noodle stir-fry

Fry strips of lean pork and ginger in low calorie cooking spray until cooked through. Add onion, peppers, broccoli florets, water chestnuts and cherry tomatoes for 1-2 minutes. Add soy sauce and snipped chives and serve with cooked dried noodles.

Ham salad sandwich, opposite

Cosy and comforting

Banish the blues, beat the cold and boost your weight loss with these warming menus.

From fish pie to steak and Slimming World chips, these healthy home-cooked classics are food for the soul – and the stomach! Curl up and plan a week of meals that will cheer you up and slim you down.